MW00413844

THE POCKET
DETECTIVE

BRITISH LIBRARY

First published in 2018 by
The British Library
96 Euston Road
London NW1 2DB

ISBN 978 0 7123 5296 3

Cataloguing in Publication Data

A catalogue record for this publication is available
from the British Library

Designed by Goldust Design
Printed and bound in Malta by Gutenberg Press

COVER IMAGE SOURCES

CONTENTS

ODD ONE OUT

Circle the text which does not fit in each list.

1. *Death of An Airman, Death in the Clouds,
   The 12.30 From Croydon, Mystery in the Channel*

2. *Somebody at the Door, The Secret of High
   Eldersham, The Cornish Coast Murder,
   Scarweather*

3. *Gaudy Night, Death Makes a Prophet,
   The Incredible Crime, Death on the Cherwell*

4. *The Hollow, Death of An Airman, The Hog's Back
   Mystery, Unnatural Death*

5. *Mystery in White, A Scream in Soho, Portrait of a
   Murderer, The Santa Klaus Murder*

KRISS KROSS
Murder in Piccadilly by Charles Kingston

Place into the grid the words listed below and then, using the letters highlighted therein, spell out the surname of an author from the British Library Crime Classics series.

4 Letters
Lies
Ruby
Soho
Wake

5 Letters
Crowd
Greed
Miser
Money
Nancy
Uncle

6 Letters
Bobbie
Dagger

Dancer
Motive

7 Letters
Cheldon

8 Letters
Kingston

9 Letters
Nightclub

10 Letters
Frozen Fang
Gold Digger
Piccadilly

11 Letters
Inheritance
Love Affairs
Nosey Ruslin

18 Letters
Underground
  Station

CROSSWORD

Solve the clues for these mystery fiction themed words. The letters in the highlighted squares spell out the surnames of two authors who are a part of the British Library Crime Classics series.

Down

1. A 1920s play based on an Agatha Christie novel. (5)

2. An event in which, usually, a police officer questions a suspicious character. (13)

3. E.g. A cigarette stub or a half-burnt letter. (4)

4. Something criminals sometimes do once their guilt has been revealed. (7)

8. There are five of these in one of Dorothy L. Sayers' titles. (3, 8)

9. An image which shows the layout of a building. (9)

10. Samuel Ratchett in Agatha Christie's *Murder on the Orient Express* is an example of such a person. (8)

11. The weapon of choice in Raymond Postgate's *Verdict of Twelve*. (6)

Across

5. Something which is not so easily washed away. (10)

6. Someone who acts unlawfully. (8)

7. The characters who could have committed the crime. (8)

10. When someone is falsely incriminated. (5-2)

12. An item which is cunningly concealed in Agatha Christie's *The Hollow*. (6)

13. An impression made by a shoe. (9)

14. A murder weapon used both in Agatha Christie's *The Murder on the Links* and *Cards on the Table*. (6)

CROSS OUT

Cross out any letters in the grid below that appear
more than once and rearrange the remaining letters
to reveal the title of an Agatha Christie novel which
also features in a British Library Crime Classics title.

K	R	W	S	H	V	T	K
C	X	Q	P	B	J	O	M
B	L	F	N	S	P	B	V
H	D	W	O	V	I	K	F
M	A	G	X	F	L	M	Z
O	J	Z	D	G	H	U	Q

WHO WAS KILLED?

Match each murder victim to the Agatha Christie
novel they appear in.

Emily Inglethorp	Murder on the Orient Express
Gerald Wade	Why Didn't They Ask Evans?
Alex Pritchard	The Mysterious Affair at Styles
Samuel Ratchett	The Murder on the Links
Arlena Marshall	The Seven Dials Mystery
Paul Renauld	Evil Under the Sun

WORD WHEEL

In ten minutes see how many words you can make using only the letters in the wheel. Words must be three letters or more and include the letter at the centre of the wheel. Plurals are not allowed and letters can only be used once. Hidden within the wheel is an author from the British Library Crime Classics series.

WORD SEARCH

All the words listed below relate to John Bude's *Death on the Riviera* (1952). The words are hidden in the grid horizontally, vertically, diagonally and backwards.

```
O D U A O M M A E N O T N E H S Y N O T
P Z R D S D C D A K I A U U D R M W A L
A Q H J U C C J H A S A H E O P V S F O
J E G Y M F O K O P O L I C E H U N T E
C I G N A R T S T N A E G R E S A N E M
M U G S B H K I T T Y K R Q K B I L A C
U O N B A W E I Y G R R N D E A M E T U
U M I R I V I E R A C Y E B D I L Y S M
C E L O V E T R I A N G L E P R A B E Y
H D G A Z A M O L A P A L L I V V E N P
A I G H T I D E R E M R O T C E P S N I
L T U S M R M Z E P J Y D G Z I E O U C
K E M O E U W P I S R E G N U O R C S T
Y R S E M C N G M T I N E E S P I Z V F
C R T C Y E N O M T I E F R E T N U O C
O A A I L O M L W W V E O M F W O A N U
B N Y N N O A R N U R M O D D I U E I W
B E U F O R G E R U O T A L R D I Z P D
E A M P Z D N E U C M E O C B O I F Y C
T N C E G R M V D F I L O U P W A P S O
T O D Q T Y O K L Y Q S J H N Y C P P E
```

Counterfeit Money	Riviera	Inspector Meredith
Blampignon	Chalky Cobbett	Nice
Sergeant Strang	Forger	Villa Paloma
Nesta	Widow	Latour
Mediterranean	Kitty	Police Hunt
Scroungers	Love Triangle	Dilys
Tony Shenton	Smuggling	

PATH FINDER PUZZLE
Portrait of a Murderer by Anne Meredith

Using the highlighted starting letter trace a path through
the letters following the order of the words listed below.

N	R	D	E	T	R	E	V	R	P	C	N
A	U	M	Y	S	Y	I	N	I	L	U	O
L	O	J	Y	T	N	I	R	T	P	S	P
I	T	I	R	E	O	M	C	A	T	E	A
N	S	C	E	L	Y	C	I	G	H	U	E
J	U	A	M	I	A	R	N	X	O	D	W
A	S	F	Y	A	D	I	M	I	N	Y	M
M	T	I	V	R	R	I	I	S	S	I	K
I	S	O	L	G	N	A	N	A	R	N	R
R	H	C	E	S	P	L	A	L	P	G	E
A	T	H	N	Y	O	L	Y	D	O	P	B
E	D	E	C	C	H	O	G	E	C	E	M

1. Adrian Gray
2. Violence
3. Death
4. Christmas
5. Family
6. Criminal
   Psychology
7. December
8. King Poplars
9. Six
10. Night
11. Pseudonym
12. Weapon
13. Culprit
14. Acrimony
15. Inverted
    Mystery
16. Journal
17. Injustice

SPOT THE TITLES

In the picture below five titles by Agatha Christie, two titles by Dorothy L. Sayers and eight titles from the British Library Crime Classics series have been jumbled up. Can you find them all?

Funeral   Miraculous   Nights

GAUDY   Murder   Seven

Third   Calamity   DEATH   Curtain   The

Guests   In

Sleeping   At

TO   ENDLESS   Mysteries

Night   Antidote   Murder

Silent   Night   DEAD

Girl   Underground   Thirteen   After

QUICK   Hotel

Kent

VENOM

UNNATURAL

Bertram's

CROSSWORD

All of the clues are for words found in titles from the British Library Crime Classics series. The highlighted letters spell out the surname of an author from the series.

Down

1. Something belonging to another country or group which seems unfamiliar and strange. (7)

3. The noise a duck makes. (5)

5. E.g. Haggai and Micah. (8)

6. A group of related things. (6)

9. Limbless or crawling animals associated with deception. (8)

11. A sudden crisis causing damage and distress. (8)

14. A word which can be preceeded by wind or succeeded by vision. (6)

16. Items of furniture used for display purposes. (6)

17. A word which can be preceded and succeeded by chair. (3)

Across

2. A word which can be succeeded by way or nail. (4)

4. Something a doctor, lawyer or detective may take on. (4)

7. Household item which appears in Agatha Christie's last title featuring Hercule Poirot. (7)

8. A word which can be found in the titles of a time-travelling trilogy from the 1980s. (4)

9. Frozen water vapour. (4)

10. Pony Express and Superior are two North American examples of this geographical feature. (4)

12. A four-sided shape. (6)

13. Wealth available to be used in the start-up of a company or in investments. (7)

15. People invited to stay in your home. (6)

17. Another word for an aviator. (6)

KRISS KROSS
Quick Curtain by Alan Melville

Place into the grid the words listed below and then, using the letters highlighted therein, spell out another title from the British Library Crime Classics series.

3 Letters	6 Letters	8 Letters
Gun	Humour	Melville
	Murder	
4 Letters	Wilson	**9 Letters**
Alan		Blue Music
Cast	**7 Letters**	Telegrams
Gwen	Critics	
Ivor	Curtain	**10 Letters**
	Cyclist	Journalist
5 Letters	Douglas	
Baker	Funeral	**12 Letters**
Props	Herbert	Scotland Yard
Stage	Inquest	Stage Manager
Derek	Suicide	
	Theatre	**13 Letters**
		Disappearances

WHO WAS KILLED?

Match each murder victim to the Dorothy L. Sayers novel they appear in.

Agatha Dawson	*The Five Red Herrings*
Philip Boyes	*Murder Must Advertise*
Paul Alexis	*Unnatural Death*
George Harrison	*The Documents in the Case*
Sandy Campbell	*Strong Poison*
Victor Dean	*Have His Carcase*

WHO AM I?

Below are five authors from the British Library Crime Classics series. Match each author to the correct fact about themselves.

A) Like his serial sleuth, this author also worked as a medical practitioner.

B) Aside from writing this author also worked in a bank.

C) This author helped to form the Crime Writers' Association.

D) Works featuring this author's serial detective were adapted for TV by the BBC in the 1960s.

E) This author, who was a railway engineer, was also an accomplished organist and choirmaster.

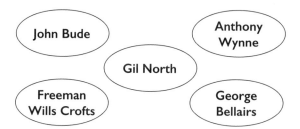

John Bude

Anthony Wynne

Gil North

Freeman Wills Crofts

George Bellairs

WORD SEARCH

All the words listed below relate to Freeman Wills Crofts' *Antidote to Venom* (1938). The words are hidden in the grid horizontally, vertically, diagonally and backwards.

C	O	N	O	O	F	A	B	N	I	S	L	L	I	W	U	Y
L	O	S	T	B	Y	C	J	P	F	R	E	N	C	H	S	W
A	Z	E	F	I	T	C	N	O	I	D	R	B	M	Y	W	T
R	T	U	D	I	B	D	A	C	D	C	R	Y	Y	T	R	V
I	A	N	T	I	H	E	R	O	U	I	G	T	A	I	E	U
S	R	E	E	R	I	H	N	O	S	I	O	P	W	L	P	E
S	A	E	U	M	X	X	A	P	I	T	N	F	E	E	I	G
A	E	S	P	L	E	U	M	O	U	P	J	I	Y	D	V	D
E	Y	G	V	P	O	L	S	T	F	O	R	C	M	I	L	I
A	E	D	R	H	A	S	Z	F	A	I	U	T	O	F	L	R
O	N	Y	C	O	N	C	E	Z	F	G	M	O	R	N	E	R
R	O	S	O	K	E	O	D	A	E	I	D	I	E	I	S	U
E	M	P	S	R	S	G	D	I	D	B	W	I	T	G	S	S
H	K	X	C	E	Q	L	S	L	V	D	M	O	K	J	U	G
G	R	E	E	D	L	N	A	E	A	A	Z	E	E	I	R	P
C	A	V	T	E	D	N	C	W	E	E	D	X	S	P	E	F
A	T	S	Y	I	D	F	I	I	I	U	S	C	H	S	Z	T
Y	R	E	T	S	Y	M	D	E	T	R	E	V	N	I	O	P

Anti Hero	Russell Viper	Embezzlement
Weymore	Poison	Clarissa
French	Inverted Mystery	Money
Midlands	George	David Capper
Surridge	Infidelity	Greed
Zoo	Crofts	Wills

SPOT THE TITLES

In the picture below five titles by Agatha Christie, two titles by Dorothy L. Sayers and eight titles from the British Library Crime Classics series have been jumbled up. Can you find them all?

In
Sparkling
CRIMES
THE
Crooked
The
Murder
Murder
THE
Tunnel
HOUSE
IS
Z
On
Detective
A
The
Death
Incredible
The
Mystery
Crime
Easy
Cherwell
Resorting
Murder
SITTAFORD
Murders
ORDEAL
Lady
INNOCENCE
Of
Advertise
POISON
Murder
By
Cyanide
THE
To
MUST
Death
Continental
Female
Strong

WORD WHEEL

In ten minutes see how many words you can make using only the letters in the wheel. Words must be three letters or more and include the letter at the centre of the wheel. Plurals are not allowed and letters can only be used once. Hidden within the wheel is a title from the British Library Crime Classics series.

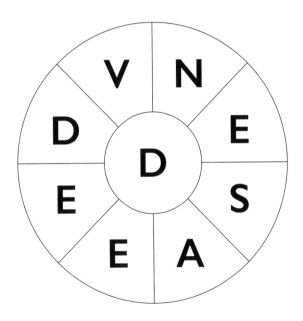

ADD A LETTER

Make a new word by adding one letter to the words on the left-hand side, with the help of the accompanying clue on the right. The letter added goes into the middle column. At the end, this column should spell out the surname of an author from the British Library Crime Classics series.

TALE	☐	A piece of furniture with four legs
CRATE	☐	To cause something to exist
POTTER	☐	Someone who schemes to do something harmful
LADE	☐	An instrument for serving soup
GRIN	☐	Any type of consumable cereal
PANT	☐	Colourful liquid used for decorating
STAND	☐	A thin thread
IDLE	☐	A sideways walk

ODD ONE OUT

Circle the text which does not fit in each list.

1. *4:50 from Paddington, Death in the Tunnel,*
   Death in the Clouds, Mystery in White

2. *Clouds of Witness, The Murder at the Vicarage,*
   Quick Curtain, The Cheltenham Square Murder

3. *The Methods of Sergeant Cluff, Murder in the*
   Museum, The Lake District Murder, The Z Murders

4. *Death of Anton, The Notting Hill Mystery, Dumb*
   Witness, Antidote to Venom

5. *Death of a Busybody, Somebody at the Door,*
   A Scream in Soho, Thirteen Guests

CROSS OUT

Cross out any letters in the grid below that appear more than once and rearrange the remaining letters to reveal the title of an Agatha Christie novel.

T	A	N	V	J	B	X	Q	P
L	W	C	S	M	D	N	O	K
D	K	Y	Q	U	G	Z	V	Y
P	Z	H	N	L	Y	C	S	J
F	X	L	W	D	K	A	N	A
N	C	J	R	Z	Q	A	M	D
Q	I	K	P	N	V	X	L	Q
W	M	A	V	D	C	E	Z	S

WORD SEARCH

All the words listed below relate to Alan Melville's *Death of Anton* (1936). The words are hidden in the grid horizontally, vertically, diagonally and backwards.

A	X	E	I	B	L	B	L	A	C	K	M	A	I	L	N	P	X
E	U	A	O	W	G	M	S	I	U	I	N	J	R	D	R	L	Y
Y	T	R	A	P	E	Z	E	A	R	T	I	S	T	S	O	H	E
Z	N	P	I	J	O	E	R	M	O	F	U	E	G	D	I	T	T
S	U	B	N	H	E	F	U	N	P	U	U	C	O	C	S	V	I
N	X	D	S	W	A	L	R	U	S	G	R	D	A	E	J	X	G
W	D	R	P	I	F	O	A	G	O	A	C	U	I	C	T	I	E
O	S	A	E	N	L	Z	R	N	S	Y	C	R	O	A	G	E	R
L	U	Y	C	A	R	A	V	A	N	S	P	R	Y	M	U	S	S
C	C	D	T	E	R	U	H	E	A	V	M	U	O	Y	U	D	R
G	R	N	O	H	A	Q	F	D	S	F	X	V	O	B	R	H	X
F	I	A	R	E	K	V	Y	R	O	E	Y	S	F	M	A	E	C
U	C	L	M	O	E	B	E	E	S	T	L	U	P	O	D	T	Y
E	S	T	I	V	Y	M	R	T	J	T	V	L	I	J	V	U	S
F	Y	O	N	J	I	E	N	A	F	F	K	F	I	R	B	P	I
G	E	C	T	R	D	E	T	E	N	F	R	D	X	V	E	Y	D
E	R	S	O	R	T	X	H	E	K	O	V	D	U	T	L	W	O
R	A	L	U	Z	E	T	N	Y	K	A	U	M	E	K	U	E	I
U	C	M	G	F	E	M	N	L	A	A	H	R	X	N	O	D	M

Tigers	Humour	Clowns
Lorimer	Acrobats	Walrus
Melville	Anton	Murder
Priest	Inspector Minto	Tents
Scotland Yard	Carey's Circus	Trapeze Artists
Theft	Caravans	Peter
Dodo	Blackmail	

28

SPOT THE TITLES

In the picture below five titles by Agatha Christie,
two titles by Dorothy L Sayers and eight titles from
the British Library Crime Classics series have been
jumbled up. Can you find them all?

Edgware   Murder   Cypress

FIVE   Family   Bodies

Of   White   BUSMAN'S   Dumb   Anton

The   In

Mystery   PIGS

DIES   Lord   HONEYMOON

Agent   Poisoned   Herrings

Foreign

Clocks   Chocolates

Red

Little   Matters   SNOW   Piccadilly

Case

Sad   The   BAZALGETTE'S

MR   Five

In   Crimson

DEATH   Witness

CROSSWORD

All of the clues are for words found in titles
from the British Library Crime Classics series.
The highlighted letters spell out the surname
of an author from the series.

Down

1. A country house with land. (5)

2. A preposition indicating the starting point. (4)

3. The final book of the New Testament. (10)

5. A word shared by a series written by Enid Blyton and a novel written by Frances Hodgson Burnett. (6)

6. A breed of chicken. (6)

9. Past tense for harming someone with a toxic substance. (8)

10. A colour which reflects nearly all rays of sunlight. (5)

12. An item which features significantly in both Christie's *Third Girl* (1966) and *Five Little Pigs* (1952). (8)

14. Another name for a killer. (8)

17. A poisonous substance secreted by scorpions. (5)

Across

4. Pronoun featuring in a Queen song of 1976. (8)

6. Loud and high-pitched noise denoting fear or anguish. (6)

7. Not making any noise. (6)

8. In a legal setting, a judgement made by a group. (7)

11. London neighbourhood which is also the name of a film starring Julia Roberts. (7, 4)

13. E.g. the Louvre and the Smithsonian Institution. (6)

15. The police rank below inspector. (8)

16. The number of clocks featuring in a 1920s novel by Agatha Christie. (5)

18. An abbreviated title for a man. (2)

19. To describe a movement which is working in secret against the ruling power. (11)

ADD A LETTER

Make a new word by adding one letter to the words on the left-hand side, with the help of the accompanying clue on the right. The letter added goes into the middle column. At the end, this column should spell out the surname of an author from the British Library Crime Classics series.

TICK ☐ Something a magician performs

SLID ☐ Has a stable shape

SADDLE ☐ To wrap material around a baby

GAVE ☐ A small hammer used by judges

FAUN ☐ The animals that live in a particular habitat or area

PATTER ☐ A decorative design

BOAR ☐ A flat and thin piece of wood

ODD ONE OUT

Circle the text which does not fit in each list.

1. *Calamity in Kent, Murder of a Lady, Cards on the Table, Murder on the Orient Express*

2. *The Sussex Downs Murder, The Hog's Back Mystery, Family Matters, Sleeping Murder*

3. *The Incredible Crime, Scarweather, Murder in Piccadilly, Hickory Dickory Dock*

4. *The Documents in the Case, The Verdict of Twelve, The Poisoned Chocolates Case, The Cornish Coast Murder*

5. *Thirteen Guests, The Sussex Downs Murder, Death on the Riviera, The Santa Klaus Murder*

WHO AM I?

Below are five authors from the British Library Crime Classics series. Match each author to the correct fact about themselves.

A) During WWI this author was a propagandist for MI7.

B) This author once brought action against a neighbour for playing chamber organ music in their rooms.

C) This author's siblings were also creative, being composers, dramatists and children's story writers.

D) This author was killed in Spain during the Civil War, where they drove ambulances.

E) This mystery writer also founded the Good Food Guide.

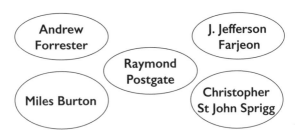

Andrew Forrester

J. Jefferson Farjeon

Raymond Postgate

Miles Burton

Christopher St John Sprigg

ADD THE VOWELS

Add in the vowels missing from each of these Agatha Christie titles. Vowels could go before, in the middle or after the letters given below.

1. MRDR S SY

2. VL NDR TH SN

3. TKN T TH FLD

4. FTR TH FNRL

5. MRDR N MSPTM

6. ND THN THR WR NN

7. CT MNG TH PGNS

8. TH PL HRS

9. T BRTMS HTL

10. LPHNTS CN RMMBR

AUTHOR ANAGRAMS

Solve the anagrams below to reveal seven authors from the British Library Crime Classics series.

1. Warren Defroster

2. First Newcomers Fall

3. Snorkeling Chats

4. Adept Gastronomy

5. Nor Light

6. Awhile Manly Stewardship

7. No Sally North

CROSS OUT

Cross out any letters in the grid below that appear more than once and rearrange the remaining letters to reveal an author from the British Library Crime Classics series.

E	A	B	Y	C	W	S	F	K
K	V	G	Q	J	A	H	D	X
X	O	C	D	M	K	Z	V	R
D	Z	W	C	Y	J	Q	G	Y
U	F	A	H	V	C	N	J	W
W	G	L	K	X	Q	Y	D	C
Y	K	J	W	V	H	A	F	I
A	Q	D	Z	T	G	W	H	X

PATH FINDER PUZZLE
Death of Anton by Alan Melville

Using the highlighted starting letter trace a path through the letters following the order of the words listed below.

A	E	L	E	E	A	L	I	O	S	P	E
T	D	V	M	S	S	E	I	N	N	T	C
H	E	I	N	Y	T	D	R	P	I	O	R
O	L	L	A	D	T	E	I	V	E	I	M
F	N	T	L	E	E	C	T	D	R	N	T
A	O	I	A	M	O	G	N	E	U	M	O
N	T	G	E	R	C	S	I	R	W	Y	C
N	T	R	A	C	C	U	D	D	E	E	O
W	Z	E	P	I	R	P	H	C	A	R	N
O	E	T	I	S	J	E	T	R	E	G	F
L	A	R	S	T	O	S	A	N	T	I	E
C	O	D	O	D	R	E	M	O	I	S	S

1. Alan Melville
2. Death of Anton
3. Tiger
4. Circus
5. Comedy
6. Sea Lion
7. Priest
8. Detective Inspector Minto
9. Confession
10. Tiger Tamer
11. Dodo
12. Clown
13. Trapeze Artists
14. Joseph Carey
15. Murder
16. Wedding

WORD WHEEL

In ten minutes see how many words you can make using only the letters in the wheel. Words must be three letters or more and include the letter at the centre of the wheel. Plurals are not allowed and letters can only be used once. Hidden within the wheel is a place mentioned in a British Library Crime Classics title.

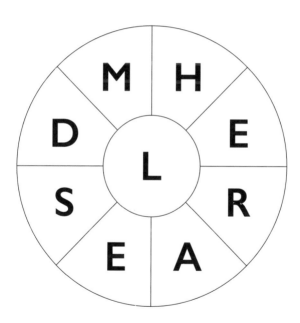

CROSSWORD

All of the clues are for words found in titles from the British Library Crime Classics series. The highlighted letters spell out the full name of an author from the series.

Down

2. A town in Gloucestershire. (10)

3. Name given to a coastline popular with holidaymakers. (7)

5. Taking an undesirable course of action through a lack of other viable options. (9)

6. Another name for corpses. (6)

7. Word which can be followed by voice and beds. (6)

9. Another name for a sleuth. (9)

14. A word which links a Jane Austen novel published in 1871 and a novel by Mary Elizabeth Braddon published nine years earlier (4).

16. A word used in radio and television to describe a band of frequencies. (7)

18. The surname which links these actors: Benny, Steven and Jonah. (4)

Across

1. A London road near Mayfair and Hyde Park. (10)

4. The name for a major tributary of the Thames, going through Oxfordshire. (8)

8. Systematic approaches used to accomplish something. (7)

10. Medicine to counteract a poison. (8)

11. Strong red colour. (7)

12. Biblical paradise where Adam and Eve temporarily resided. (4)

13. An illegal action. (5)

14. Adjective used to describe distance and time. (4)

15. An administrative area. (8)

17. The state of no longer living. (5)

19. Word which can be succeeded by breakfast and quilt. (11)

KRISS KROSS
The Sussex Downs Murder by John Bude

Place into the grid the words listed below and then,
using the letters highlighted therein, spell out another
novel by Bude, which is also a part of the British
Library Crime Classics series.

3 Letters
Car
Cap

4 Letters
Bude
Farm
Hoax
John
Lime

5 Letters
Bones
Bride
Kilns
Major
Oyler

6 Letters
Corpse
Petrol
Rother
Sussex

7 Letters
Holiday
William
Village

8 Letters
Brothers
Foul Play
Meredith
Thornton

9 Letters
Blenkings

10 Letters
Chalklands

11 Letters
Slippery Sid

ADD A LETTER

Make a new word by adding one letter to the words on the left-hand side, with the help of the accompanying clue on the right. The letter added goes into the middle column. At the end, this column should spell out a location mentioned in the title of a British Library Crime Classics novel.

ACHE ☐ A place where hidden items are stored

GABBLE ☐ To grope or feel around with your hands

SLOP ☐ A type of boat

EARN ☐ To really desire or want something

ITCH ☐ A narrow trench often found at the sides of roads or fields

PINE ☐ To give an opinion

SAIL ☐ A mollusc which carries its home on its back

CROSS OUT

Cross out any letters in the grid below that appear more than once and rearrange the remaining letters to reveal a short story writer from the British Library Crime Classics series.

E	D	T	Z	J	U	W	S	A
F	W	Q	K	M	D	N	R	T
J	S	H	G	I	X	P	Z	F
Z	G	D	V	F	S	G	K	Q
X	R	N	T	J	U	O	M	X
V	K	L	O	D	F	C	W	S
T	F	S	Q	M	N	P	R	J
B	U	W	V	G	T	Z	D	Y

WHO WAS KILLED?

Match each murder victim to the Agatha Christie
novel they appear in.

Louise Leidner	Hercule Poirot's Christmas
Mr Shaitana	A Murder is Announced
Linnet Doyle	Sparkling Cyanide
Simeon Lee	Cards on the Table
Rosemary Barton	Murder in Mesopotamia
Rudi Scherz	Death on the Nile

AUTHOR ANAGRAMS

Solve the anagrams below to reveal seven authors from the British Library Crime Classics series.

1. Nimble Tours

2. An All Evil Elm

3. Crinkled Roamer

4. Soggier Relabel

5. Yet Nobly Hearken

6. A Guiltiness Hole

7. Soldiery Via Ham

KRISS KROSS
Continental Crimes

Place into the grid the words listed below and then, using the letters highlighted therein, spell out another short story collection in the British Library Crime Classics series.

4 Letters
Bell
Room

5 Letters
Doyle
Lover
Stacy
Tower
Villa

6 Letters
Arnold
Belloc
Bruges
Dinner

Garden
Popeau
Secret

7 Letters
Counter
Farjeon
Gilbert
Perfect

8 Letters
Aumonier
Bracelet
Catacomb
Christie
Tennyson

9 Letters
Stacpoole

10 Letters
Chesterton

11 Letters
Continental

CROSSWORD

All of the clues are for words found in the titles and
authors contained in the British Library short story
collection *Serpents in Eden*. The highlighted letters spell
out the surname of an author from the series.

Down

1. One of Dorothy's companions in *The Wizard of Oz*. (9)

5. A way to describe the quickest and most undeviating route to a place. (6)

6. Word which completes these titles: — *in White* and *The Sittaford* —. (7)

8. A defamatory comment about another, leaving the speaker open to being sued. (7)

9. The outer wall of a castle. (6)

11. A handcart street vendors use. (6)

13. The surname of one of the suspects in the game Cluedo. (7)

14. What police look for at the scene of the crime. (8)

16. An investigation into an undesirable event to ascertain the facts concerning it, especially causes. (7)

Across

2. Sleeveless garment for protecting clothes. (6)

3. Public event involving historical reenactment. (7)

4. An intense but short-lived enthusiasm for something. (3)

7. A word which can be followed by war and vote. (5)

10. The surname of the victim in the game Cluedo (UK edition). (5)

12. An occupation involving bobbers and lures. (9)

15. Socially appropriate. (6)

17. An expert in natural history. (10)

18. A synonym for authentic and sincere. (7)

19. The narrator's occupation in Agatha Christie's *The Murder of Roger Ackroyd*. (6)

51

CROSS OUT

Cross out any letters in the grid below that appear more than once and rearrange the remaining letters to reveal the surname of an author from the British Library Crime Classics series.

B	Z	T	D	Q	C	K	R	U
U	K	W	H	L	X	G	V	B
P	F	I	Y	E	Z	C	I	Q
Z	V	Q	G	H	K	M	Y	N
T	I	C	X	B	D	U	L	T
L	P	M	O	T	Y	H	W	P
C	W	K	V	L	Q	G	A	K
J	B	D	U	Z	P	I	X	D

WHO WAS KILLED?

Match each murder victim to the Agatha Christie
novel they appear in.

John Christow	*Cat Among the Pigeons*
Gladys Martin	*They Do It With Mirrors*
Aristide Leonides	*The Hollow*
Grace Springer	*Crooked House*
Father Gorman	*A Pocket Full of Rye*
Alex Restarick	*The Pale Horse*

CROSS OUT

Cross out any letters in the grid below that appear more than once and rearrange the remaining letters to reveal an author from the British Library Crime Classics series.

N	A	F	K	I	M	U	C	L
C	L	P	R	T	X	F	V	A
I	G	Y	K	J	R	P	K	P
M	V	A	C	P	T	S	W	E
P	S	D	Z	Q	G	A	R	F
O	F	X	M	I	R	C	T	I
R	K	V	L	W	Y	Z	H	M
Q	T	G	B	F	P	S	X	Q

ADD A LETTER

Make a new word by adding one letter to the words on the left-hand side, with the help of the accompanying clue on the right. The letter added goes into the middle column. At the end, this column should spell out the full name of an author from the British Library Crime Classics series.

RUMP ☐ To act in a sulky manner

LARD ☐ A person who owns an estate in Scotland

PUCK ☐ To quickly remove something

SPLIT ☐ Something which is used to immobilise and support a broken bone

FLAT ☐ To remain on the surface of a liquid

STAY ☐ A domestic animal without a home

READ ☐ The way someone walks or the sound that they make when they do

SACK ☐ A roughly made cabin

LOCATION, LOCATION, LOCATION

Match each location to the Agatha Christie novel it appears in.

Devon	Destination Unknown
Dartmoor	The Moving Finger
Cape Town	Evil Under the Sun
Lymstock	A Murder is Announced
Morocco	The Sittaford Mystery
Chipping Cleghorn	The Man in the Brown Suit

WORD WHEEL

In ten minutes see how many words you can make using only the letters in the wheel. Words must be three letters or more and include the letter at the centre of the wheel. Plurals are not allowed and letters can only be used once. Hidden within the wheel is a word commonly found in mystery fiction.

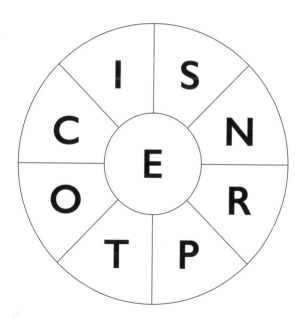

PATH FINDER PUZZLE
Thirteen Guests by J. Jefferson Farjeon

Using the highlighted starting letter trace a path through
the letters following the order of the words listed below.

J	O	F	O	S	A	N	L	A	T	I	O
E	H	N	K	S	R	G	U	E	R	T	N
N	I	D	E	N	T	S	Y	S	S	C	A
E	R	A	N	D	L	P	T	O	J	A	L
S	I	D	N	A	L	A	R	U	R	N	I
R	N	I	A	I	C	I	I	R	N	I	S
O	G	P	O	L	I	T	H	T	N	D	T
H	N	T	R	U	O	C	T	E	E	R	L
A	I	D	O	O	R	Y	N	E	E	V	O
R	L	A	G	P	T	E	C	O	U	N	T
T	I	D	V	T	R	L	R	B	U	O	R
M	S	N	A	I	A	G	A	E	S	H	Y

1. Thirteen	10. Nadine
2. Country House	11. John Foss
3. Bragley Court	12. Kendall
4. Dog	13. Party
5. Portrait	14. Strangulation
6. Vandalism	15. Actress
7. Train	16. Journalist
8. Horse Riding	17. Dinner
9. Politician	18. Love

ODD ONE OUT

Circle the text which does not fit in each list.

1. *Sergeant Cluff Stands Firm, Have His Carcase,
   Mystery in the Channel, Murder of a Quack*

2. *Murder Must Advertise, Scarweather, Seven Dead,
   The Five Red Herrings*

3. *Whose Body?, Thirteen Guests, The Santa Klaus
   Murder, Portrait of a Killer*

4. *The Labours of Hercules, Murder at the Manor,
   The Notting Hill Mystery, Foreign Bodies*

5. *Murder in the Museum, Death of Anton,
   Death on the Cherwell, Murder of a Lady*

CROSSWORD

All of the clues are for words found in the titles contained in the British Library short story collection *Capital Crimes*. The highlighted letters spell out the surname of an author from the series.

Down

1. Both the Taj Mahal and the Parthenon are made from this substance. (6)

2. A heavy piece of artillery. (6)

4. The antonym of bumpy and uneven. (4)

5. A milk-based food product. (6)

6. The word can be preceded by fleet and suceeded by map and fighter. (6)

8. Many of these make a task quicker to complete. (5)

9. E.g. a jigsaw or Rubik's cube. (6)

11. There are three of this item within Shakespeare's *The Merchant of Venice*, for characters to choose between. (6)

12. Item of clothing that superheroes wear to conceal their identity. (4)

15. Where photosynthesis mainly occurs within a plant. (4)

Across

3. Can come in types such as planetary and trade. (4)

6. A metal which has the atomic number 47. (6)

7. Something you can do with clothes and pictures. (4)

10. The word which completes these titles by Agatha Christie: *Peril at End* — and *Crooked* —. (5)

11. One of the two card types you can pick up in the game Monopoly. (6)

13. The direction of the wind which brings P. L. Travers' character, Mary Poppins, to the Banks family. (4)

14. E.g. Shakespeare's *Othello* and John Webster's *The Duchess of Malfi*. (7)

16. A synonym for small or tiny. (6)

ADD A LETTER

Make a new word by adding one letter to the
words on the left-hand side, with the help of the
accompanying clue on the right. The letter added
goes into the middle column. At the end, this column
should spell out a location mentioned in the title of a
British Library Crime Classics novel.

ROOF		Synonym of evidence
MOST		When something is slightly wet
RACK		Loud, sudden and explosive noise
RAVEN		Another way of describing a cowardly person
PAST		A food with Italian origins
RIFT		To slowly move with no specific direction, often at the behest of outside forces
PLAN		Often used to describe simple cooking
OATH		To be reluctant to do something
GOAT		To delight in someone else's misfortunes
EAST		The ingredient which makes bread rise

WORD SEARCH

All the words listed below relate to William Stephens Hayward's *Revelations of a Lady Detective* (1864). The words are hidden in the grid horizontally, vertically, diagonally and backwards.

```
F E M A L E S L E U T H F O D D H A O I O V
H C C O I Z J T O L S M Z U A R R M E U N R
E L M N T I Z F T R O X Y P S I A J Z O U T
L O I M A N T U A N I B T E I E E W X O N N
O Z P E N N Y D R E A D F U L R W P Y U F O
D U I N C O G N I T A M F P A D I E Z A E O
S E C R E T S O C I E T Y N O D J I R X H T
E P D O E S I H U C O L O N E L W A R N E R
Q C G O P L P R G N U S Y R U A M K P A M C
B U N D E R C O V E R W O R K Z N I O T P V
U R M A O F P O L I C E C O N S U L T A N T
S H O R T S T O R I E S Q M C S O A C Z S X
R B N F S I R P P C N D C U V S N E G E A G
F H I N C P R X E J F U Y J I I Y I E P K Y
N Y J T C N A E G M E W Y I Z T O T K A S L
U F U M H F I S H O A A E R K K E G O R G S
Q X D S Z E U G C N T E L I E I U D M A O U
A T X U V S P N I H I H U O B B A G L Q O P
R E W E L C E L T S A C I T U T B X P O Q I
E G P L K T U F Y L O L E C B S E O I R V C
E V E L Y N S T V I N C E N T S Y I R H S E
L N H T L A E W L D D B M S J X R F E P M S
```

Inheritance	Short Stories	Jealousy
Female Sleuth	Gothic	Castle Clewer
Robbery	Penny Dreadful	Incognita
Zini	Mantuani	Porkins
Hayward	Mrs Paschal	Colonel Warner
Wealth	Police Consultant	Undercover Work
Unrequited Love	Evelyn St Vincent	
Sewer	Secret Society	

WHO AM I?

Below are five authors from the British Library Crime Classics series. Match each author to the correct fact about themselves.

A) Aside from mystery writing this author also wrote on their other passion: rural crafts.

B) This author has a bus in Brighton named after them.

C) Later in life this author became a Unitarian minister.

D) This Australian author was a heavyweight boxer before becoming a writer.

E) This Welsh author's real name was Colwyn Edward Vulliamy.

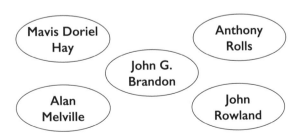

Mavis Doriel Hay

Anthony Rolls

John G. Brandon

Alan Melville

John Rowland

DISTORTED COVERS 1

Guess which British Library Crime Classics cover is shown below.

DISTORTED COVERS 2

Guess which British Library Crime Classics cover is shown below.

BRITISH *LIBRARY* CRIME CLASSICS

DISTORTED COVERS 3

Guess which British Library Crime Classics cover is shown below.

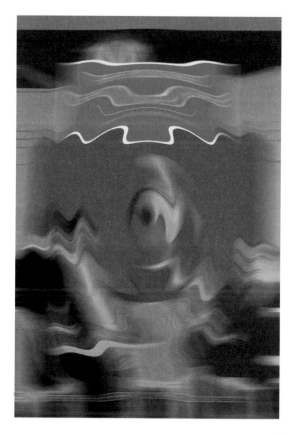

DISTORTED COVERS 4

Guess which British Library Crime Classics cover is shown below.

BRITISH LIBRARY CRIME CLASSICS

DISTORTED COVERS 5

Guess which British Library Crime Classics cover is shown below.

DISTORTED COVERS 6

Guess which British Library Crime Classics cover is shown below.

DISTORTED COVERS 7

Guess which British Library Crime Classics cover is shown below.

DISTORTED COVERS 8

Guess which British Library Crime Classics cover is shown below.

DISTORTED COVERS 9

Guess which British Library Crime Classics cover
is shown below.

SPOT THE DIFFERENCE

Can you find the 15 changes which have been made to the British Library Crime Classics cover on the right?

VERDICT OF
TWELVE

RAYMOND POSTGATE

BRITISH LIBRARY CRIME CLASSICS

VERDICT OF
TWLEVE

RAYMOND POSGATE

BRITISH LIBRARY CRIME CLASSICS

75

SPOT THE DIFFERENCE

Can you find the 15 changes which have been made to the British Library Crime Classics cover on the right?

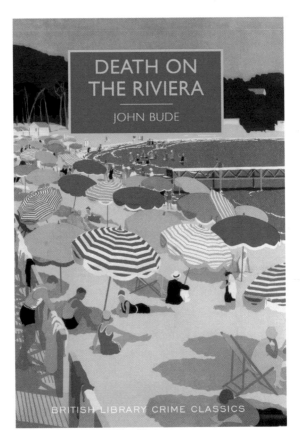

DEATH ON
THE RIVIERA

JOHN BUDE

BRITISH LIBRARY CRIME CLASSICS

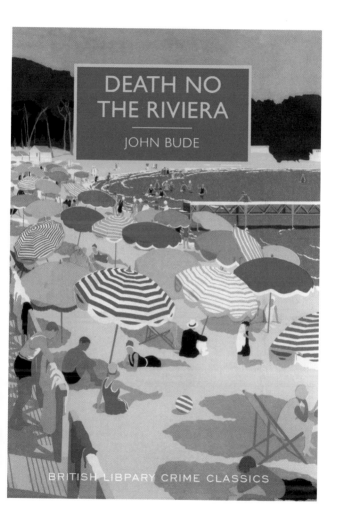

DEATH NO
THE RIVIERA

JOHN BUDE

BRITISH LIBPARY CRIME CLASSICS

SPOT THE DIFFERENCE

Can you find the 15 changes which have been made to the British Library Crime Classics cover on the right?

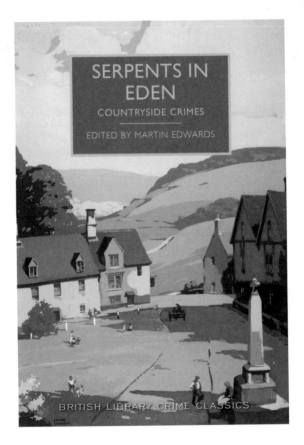

SERPENTS IN EDEN

COUNTRYSIDE CRIMES

EDITED BY MARTIN EDWARDS

BRITISH LIBRARY CRIME CLASSICS

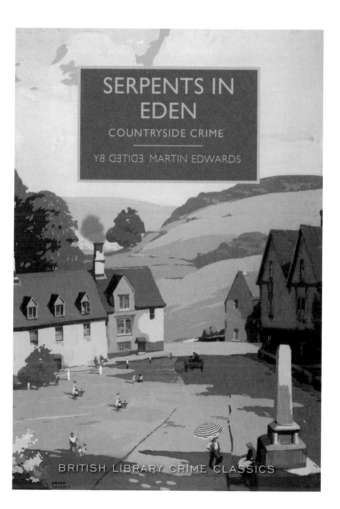

SERPENTS IN
EDEN

COUNTRYSIDE CRIME

EDITED BY MARTIN EDWARDS

SPOT THE DIFFERENCE

Can you find the 15 changes which have been made to the British Library Crime Classics cover on the right?

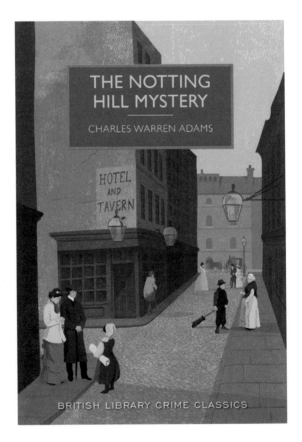

THE NOTTING
HILL MYSTERY

CHARLES WARREN ADAMS

HOTEL
AND
TAVERN

BRITISH LIBRARY CRIME CLASSICS

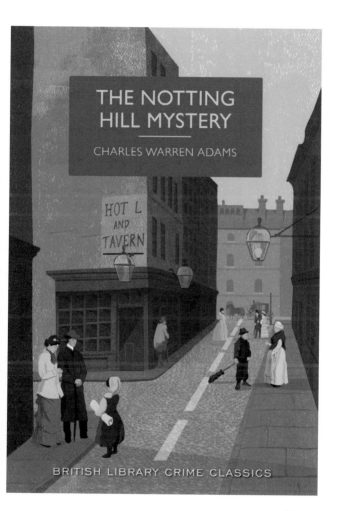

THE NOTTING HILL MYSTERY

CHARLES WARREN ADAMS

HOT L
AND
TAVERN

BRITISH LIBRARY CRIME CLASSICS

SPOT THE DIFFERENCE

Can you find the 15 changes which have been made to the British Library Crime Classics cover on the right?

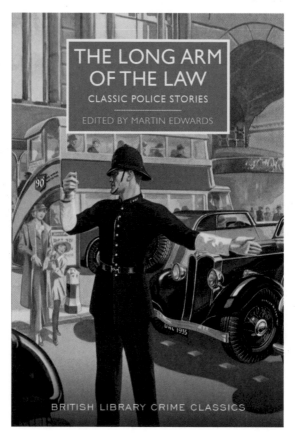

THE LONG ARM
OF THE LAW

CLASSIC POLICE STORIES

EDITED BY MARTIN EDWARDS

BRITISH LIBRARY CRIME CLASSICS

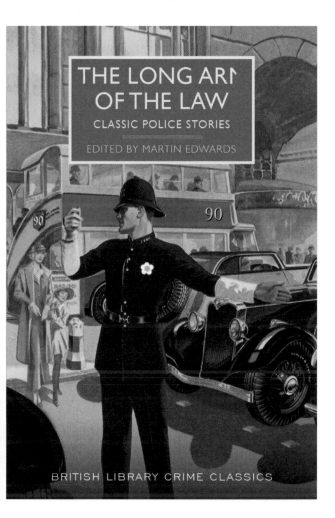

THE LONG ARM
OF THE LAW

CLASSIC POLICE STORIES

EDITED BY MARTIN EDWARDS

SPOT THE DIFFERENCE

Can you find the 15 changes which have been made to the British Library Crime Classics cover on the right?

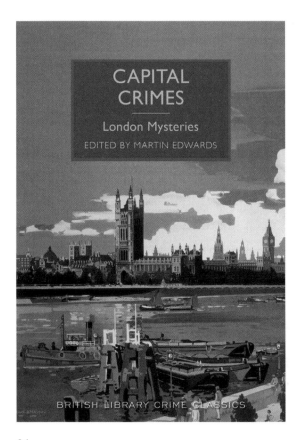

CAPITAL
CRIMES

London Mysteries

EDITED BY MARTIN EDWARDS

BRITISH LIBRARY CRIME CLASSICS

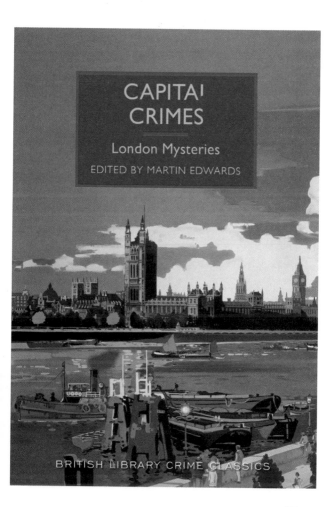

CAPITAL
CRIMES

London Mysteries

EDITED BY MARTIN EDWARDS

BRITISH LIBRARY CRIME CLASSICS

SPOT THE DIFFERENCE

Can you find the 15 changes which have been made to the British Library Crime Classics cover on the right?

QUICK
CURTAIN

ALAN MELVILLE

BRITISH LIBRARY CRIME CLASSICS

QUICK
CURTAIN

ALAN MELVILLE

SPOT THE DIFFERENCE

Can you find the 15 changes which have been made to the British Library Crime Classics cover on the right?

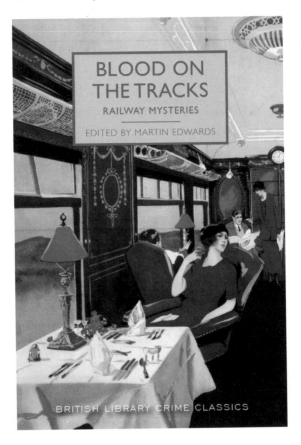

BLOOD ON
THE TRACKS

RAILWAY MYSTERIES

EDITED BY MARTIN EDWARDS

BRITISH LIBRARY CRIME CLASSICS

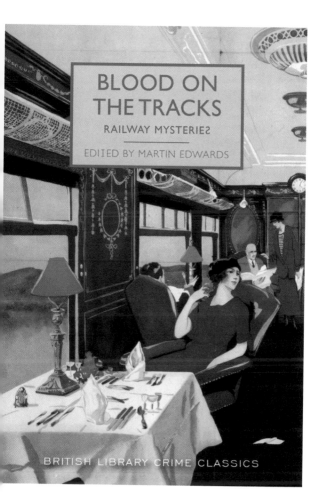

BLOOD ON
THE TRACKS

RAILWAY MYSTERIES

EDITED BY MARTIN EDWARDS

BRITISH LIBRARY CRIME CLASSICS

SNAPSHOT COVERS I

Guess the five British Library Crime Classics shown below.

SNAPSHOT COVERS 2

Guess the five British Library Crime Classics
shown below.

SNAPSHOT COVERS 3

Guess the five British Library Crime Classics
shown below.

SNAPSHOT COVERS 4

Guess the five British Library Crime Classics
shown below.

SNAPSHOT COVERS 5

Guess the five British Library Crime Classics shown below.

SNAPSHOT COVERS 6

Guess the five British Library Crime Classics shown below.

KRISS KROSS
Revelations of a Lady Detective
by William Stephens Hayward

Place into the grid the words listed below and then, using the letters highlighted therein, spell out a title from the British Library Crime Classics series.

3 Letters	7 Letters	9 Letters
Nun	Drowned	Detective
	Hayward	Incognita
4 Letters	Letters	Victorian
Gang	Paschal	Whitehall
Heir		Crinoline
Will	8 Letters	
	Countess	10 Letters
5 Letters	Diamonds	Kidnapping
Sewer	Disguise	
Theft	Identity	
	Revolver	
6 Letters	Vervaine	
Female		
Reward		
Warner		

ODD ONE OUT

Circle the text which does not fit in each list.

1. *The Murder of My Aunt, Antidote to Venom,*
   Somebody at the Door, Family Matters

2. *Excellent Intentions, Weekend at Thrackley,*
   The Verdict of Twelve, Sad Cypress

3. *Murder in Piccadilly, A Scream in Soho,*
   Somebody at the Door, The Dead Shall Be Raised

4. *Fire in the Thatch, Evil Under the Sun,*
   The Sittaford Mystery, Bats in the Belfry

5. *Death Makes a Prophet, Cards on the Table,*
   Portrait of a Murderer, The Lake District Murder

PATH FINDER PUZZLE
Somebody at the Door by
Raymond Postgate

Using the highlighted starting letter trace a path through the letters following the order of the words listed below.

S	C	E	S	E	A	S	U	I	T	C
E	H	L	E	V	G	D	O	R	E	S	A
E	A	R	T	U	S	R	B	I	N	S	P
Y	O	L	T	M	T	A	B	Y	R	O	E
I	R	P	M	E	S	N	E	R	H	T	C
H	D	C	L	M	O	A	L	L	O	M	E
T	I	A	S	S	R	Y	W	T	I	R
S	N	R	T	G	G	E	G	A	R	F	E
E	W	E	N	N	E	O	R	L	U	U	E
G	A	H	R	I	L	Y	E	T	D	G	E
L	O	R	Y	G	R	A	R	J	A	Y	R
L	I	C	N	U	O	C	Y	A	N	U	A

1. January
2. Adultery
3. Councillor
4. Henry Grayling
5. Train
6. Wages
7. Third Class
8. George Ransom
9. Employees
10. Charles Evett
11. Mustard Gas
12. Suitcase
13. Robbery
14. Inspector Holly
15. Wartime
16. Refugee

99

CROSSWORD

All of the clues are for words found in the titles
and authors contained in the British Library short
story collection *Resorting to Murder*. The highlighted
letters spell out the full name of an author from the
series.

Down

1. To move furtively away from someone. (4)

2. The surname of the woman Edward VII married. (7)

3. The word which completes this Christie title set in Merlinville-sur-Mer: *The Murder on the —* (5)

5. A synonym for an assignment or job. (4)

6. The word which completes this American title for a Christie novel: *A — for Murder* (7).

7. To have something taken away. (7)

9. An exciting experience, often in dangerous or exotic places. (9)

10. A unit of measurement for distilled spirits. (6)

12. Collective term for foreign countries. (6)

15. An object famously removed from Westminster Abbey in 1950. (5)

17. Blade used for hair removal. (5)

Across

4. An informal term for both diamonds and cocaine. (3)

8. The occupation of James Hilton's character Mr Chipping. (12)

11. The familial connection between Jane Austen's characters Colonel Fitzwilliam and Mr Darcy.

13. A make of car known for its luxuriousness. (7)

14. Jack Nicklaus is famous for his skill in this sport. (4)

16. A form of reasoning which starts with an effect and works back to its causes. (10)

18. A type of nut. (5)

19. Gout commonly affects this part of the body. (4)

WORD SEARCH

All the words listed below relate to Anthony Berkeley's *The Poisoned Chocolates Case* (1929). The words are hidden in the grid horizontally, vertically, diagonally and backwards.

```
I  T  F  N  E  S  T  C  K  E  T  J  V  I  E  R  Y  D  O  Q  E  S  V
C  I  S  Y  B  E  R  K  E  L  E  Y  P  U  L  T  I  Y  M  U  U  S  L
E  U  M  U  F  R  M  A  R  M  M  P  A  J  J  E  O  M  M  B  Z  E  O
U  C  S  C  E  E  E  Z  J  F  P  L  L  P  D  I  O  U  D  E  O  N  C
P  E  S  H  T  U  E  L  S  R  U  E  T  A  M  A  A  O  I  N  F  L  G
F  N  M  E  G  N  E  V  E  R  W  T  S  I  L  E  V  O  N  D  I  U  A
A  M  B  R  O  S  E  C  H  I  T  T  E  R  W  I  C  K  I  I  E  F  P
A  S  U  O  T  D  V  A  O  S  B  S  F  A  E  Z  I  R  B  X  L  H  N
W  P  O  E  D  L  D  W  E  A  E  C  R  P  Q  Q  U  Y  U  T  D  T  T
N  N  I  D  V  I  R  U  D  S  A  T  A  E  I  S  I  K  G  S  E  I  H
M  L  C  X  C  X  O  S  Q  E  N  Q  A  M  M  K  P  B  Y  S  R  A  G
R  E  T  S  I  R  R  A  B  E  Q  O  E  L  A  M  R  N  H  F  F  I
H  C  Y  M  Q  Z  X  R  L  B  L  A  I  E  O  S  A  E  Y  E  L  N  R
B  B  H  H  T  G  L  A  U  A  E  O  A  T  G  C  R  D  L  A  E  U  W
O  P  E  N  N  E  F  A  T  H  E  R  A  Z  U  I  O  F  E  I  M  M  Y
G  F  O  M  Q  U  M  Y  A  U  N  U  I  S  N  L  A  H  K  C  M  A  A
C  R  I  M  E  S  C  I  R  C  L  E  U  G  A  S  O  N  C  A  I  P  L
D  A  R  K  H  U  M  O  U  R  D  U  H  D  I  R  W  S  A  U  N  L  P
D  P  Y  T  I  L  I  B  I  L  L  A  F  H  T  U  E  L  S  I  G  A  A
T  H  E  A  T  R  E  S  R  X  M  A  I  U  Q  S  P  O  I  S  O  N  E
Y  B  S  E  R  O  M  R  O  T  C  E  P  S  N  I  F  E  I  H  C  A  V
O  X  U  A  T  N  M  O  X  Y  I  U  W  R  Z  D  T  Q  A  K  E  U  F
M  S  O  G  G  K  I  E  O  M  O  R  A  O  Y  A  N  Y  H  S  X  O  N
```

Unfaithfulness	Dark Humour	Playwright
Amateur Sleuths	Novelist	Theatre
Bendix	Ambrose Chitterwick	Solutions
Sheringham	Chief Inspector Moresby	Poison
Revenge	Fielder-Flemming	Berkeley
Chocolates	Pennefather	Barrister
Sleuth Fallibility	Crimes Circle	Alice Dammers

ADD A LETTER

Make a new word by adding one letter to the words on the left-hand side, with the help of the accompanying clue on the right. The letter added goes into the middle column. At the end, this column should spell out the setting of a novel from the British Library Crime Classics series.

BAY	☐	A young human
DUNK	☐	Antonym of sober
AWNING	☐	An involuntary reflex often caused by tiredness or boredom
BUGLE	☐	To carry out a task poorly
COMA	☐	To indicate a pause when writing
SLY	☐	To violently kill someone
SERVE	☐	To abruptly change direction when driving to avoid a collision
TOUGH	☐	Drinking receptacle for animals

LOCATION, LOCATION, LOCATION

Match each location to the British Library Crime Classic they appear in.

Birmingham Zoo	*Portrait of a Murderer*
Shufflecester	*Death on the Cherwell*
King Poplars	*Death of a Busybody*
Oxford	*Antidote to Venom*
Hilary Magna	*The Incredible Crime*
Cambridge	*Family Matters*

WORD WHEEL

In ten minutes see how many words you can make using only the letters in the wheel. Words must be three letters or more and include the letter at the centre of the wheel. Plurals are not allowed and letters can only be used once. Hidden within the wheel is a word commonly found in mystery fiction and also in a British Library Crime Classics title.

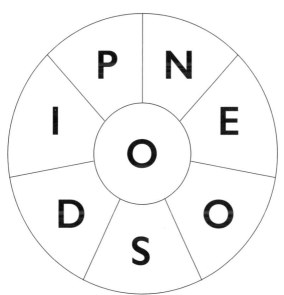

PATH FINDER PUZZLE
The Cheltenham Square Murder
by John Bude

Using the highlighted starting letter trace a path through the letters following the order of the words listed below.

O	W	H	D	R	P	E	R	O	M	T	S
R	L	O	E	A	R	A	R	C	L	E	E
R	I	R	E	T	M	K	C	H	E	R	N
A	D	T	M	T	A	I	A	E	R	Y	A
S	A	Y	I	R	E	L	L	R	U	M	L
R	U	O	S	S	B	N	B	D	E	R	D
E	D	B	H	G	O	O	A	M	R	E	O
R	I	T	H	I	E	N	P	U	M	M	U
E	M	T	R	E	G	E	N	S	E	B	S
N	T	N	E	E	T	Y	C	A	R	A	R
I	E	N	D	R	I	S	Q	U	R	C	N
R	E	P	U	S	R	W	E	M	I	T	E

1. Ernest Elmore
2. Archery
3. Aldous Barnet
4. Crime Writer
5. Superintendent Meredith
6. Regency Square
7. Summer
8. Murder
9. Map
10. Neighbours
11. Arrow
12. Holiday
13. Tree
14. Dr Pratt
15. Miss Boon
16. Blackmailer

106

WORD WHEEL

In ten minutes see how many words you can make using only the letters in the wheel. Words must be three letters or more and include the letter at the centre of the wheel. Plurals are not allowed and letters can only be used once. Hidden within the wheel is a key word from a British Library Crime Classics title.

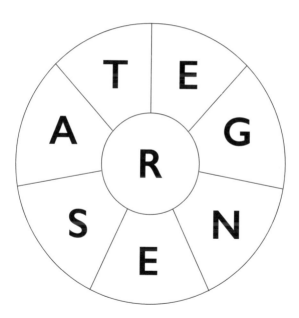

KRISS KROSS
Murder in the Museum by John Rowland

Place into the grid the words listed below and then,
using the letters highlighted therein, spell out a title from
the British Library Crime Classics series.

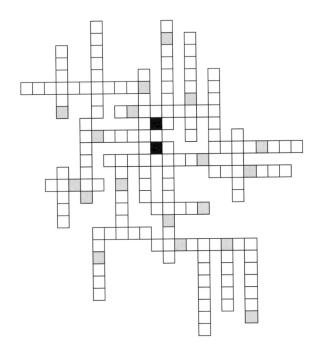

5 Letters
Angus
Baker
Sarah
Moses

6 Letters
Arnell
Fiancé
Museum
Violet

7 Letters
Almonds
Crocker
Cyanide
Man Hunt
Rowland
Shelley

8 Letters
Evidence
Poisoner
Reporter

9 Letters
Abduction
Academics
Daydreams
Fairhurst
Yorkshire

10 Letters
Cunningham

11 Letters
Millionaire
Reading Room

WORD WHEEL

In ten minutes see how many words you can make using only the letters in the wheel. Words must be three letters or more and include the letter at the centre of the wheel. Plurals are not allowed and letters can only be used once. Hidden within the wheel is the surname of an author from the British Library Crime Classics series.

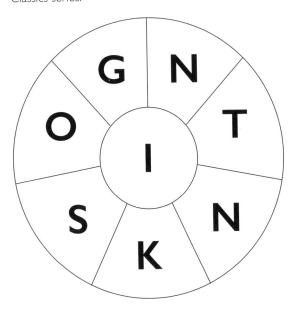

WORD SEARCH

All the words listed below relate to John G Brandon's
A Scream in Soho (1940). The words are hidden in
the grid horizontally, vertically, diagonally and
backwards.

```
A Y L S Y M T E F R K M C S V I R J J Q
Y N D T O N N E I N O D N A R B A O I O
B Y D N U C L I E U H A S I A N E C C V
I A A F U D S E M A D A M T A W M T A H
G D D O P H O N E Y W A R P P N E M R I
B F A Y A O O E A Q Y O O N O K E O I N
I V N P O Y E S E L T O E E C O S D S S
L E N A R N E F O A P V Z O S A O T T P
L G Y D E C Z P I C Y N P R Y T H E O E
O W T R A W D L R O W K E S K D O S C C
W M H M O P L U S S C T T L S V G S R T
O A E N I Q S E O I S I F F O G W A A O
T I D A M C I L P G L Y A E U T I D T R
E U I R P P O E N E V U O Y F O S O S M
A L P E S Y U A T M I I O J T C U M X C
M U P L O O G T X F V T Z A G T A E N C
O D K L I C O R E F U G E E S E V N Y A
U W T I B L A C K O U T S E C T P I E R
A I C R F I O N F E S M C Y S J D C H T
E G E H L O R Y O N E O P R A Y C O R H
P N S T Y A I L G O D A P S A I C U L Y
```

Brandon
World War Two
Spies
Danny the Dip
Aristocrats
Big Bill
Pick Pocket

Soho
Inspector McCarthy
Gangsters
Madame
Tessa Domenico
Ludwig
Phoney War

Blackouts
Stiletto
Stolen Plans
Thriller
Lucia Spadoglia
Refugees

KRISS KROSS
Scarweather by Anthony Rolls

Place into the grid the words listed below and then, using the letters highlighted therein, spell out the surnames of two authors in the British Library Crime Classics series.

4 Letters
Eric

5 Letters
Chess
Coast
Hilda
Rolls

6 Letters
Cousin
Reisby
Tumuli
Watson

7 Letters
Barrows
Burials
Science

8 Letters
Jealousy
Suspense

9 Letters
Artefacts
Barrister
Ellingham
Professor

11 Letters
Archaeology
Farringdale
Scarweather

12 Letters
Superstition

13 Letters
Retrospective

CROSSWORD

All of the clues are for words found in titles
from the British Library Crime Classics series.
The highlighted letters spell out the full name of
an author from the series.

Down

1. The type of the six things the Queen in *Alice's Adventures in Wonderland* thinks of before breakfast. (10)

2. The coldest season of the year. (6)

3. To selfishly consume or take most or all of something. (3)

4. The premeditated killing of another person. (6)

6. A modal verb commenting on future events. (5)

9. Fast, often attributed to movement. (5)

12. Someone who acts on behalf of another person. (5)

14. The number of pairs of ribs that humans normally have. (6)

16. Another word for product trade names. (5)

18. A way to describe an attitude which is strongly felt and unlikely to change. (4)

Across

5. Someone who inteferes or pries into other people's affairs. (8)

7. The word which completes these songs: '— Baby' (1953) and 'Must be —' (1960). (5)

8. A borough of London. (7)

10. A system of rules which govern a country. (3)

11. Divinely remarkable, though unlikely. (10)

13. The surname of Superman's alias. (4)

15. Confectionary found within a box. (10)

17. Land ajoining the sea. (5)

19. The age a Jewish boy becomes a bar mitzvah. (8)

20. A sow, hen and a jenny are all the — of their species. (6)

ADD A LETTER

Make a new word by adding one letter to the words on the left-hand side, with the help of the accompanying clue on the right. The letter added goes into the middle column. At the end, this column should spell out the surname of a serial sleuth used by an author in the British Library Crime Classics series.

THEE	☐	Reoccurring melody in a song
STEM	☐	Healthy way to cook vegetables
ORAL	☐	Aquatic addition to a necklace
BRIE	☐	Key member at a wedding
DROP	☐	What flowers do when they die
GRID	☐	To crush into small particles
RELY	☐	Collaborative running race
FATTEN	☐	To smooth something out
CARE	☐	Group of people trained for a purpose

WORD SEARCH

All the words listed below relate to Mavis Doriel Hay's *Murder Underground* (1934). The words are hidden in the grid horizontally, vertically, diagonally and backwards.

```
T C J T P K X I H C T L S C S I X C L E
N A I J D E T R A E H T H G I L A G E Y
I T H R R Y F D K T R E H D F V O R T P
R M C U D N A M B A S I L A I P P C O P
P M B I N E F I Y O F O I O Y F A P H U
T E D A L N F I O R T P O T I T R O N T
O I G G O U Y O R S U E E U U K J L O R
O P O L U Y E O U I D Y O T J D Y X T E
F D U N D R I A C R O T C E P S N I P E
P E A R L N E C K L A C E D M X T H M U
H O A I Y A H L E I R O D S I V A M A T
C J E S T I R E D H E R R I N G S F R U
Y S W B K A J R N N M S N Y D T E D F B
C C D I S I N H E R I T A N C E Y S C E
P O N G L E T O N T G R U D G E S L I S
Y R A K Y F O A Y O S I Y M B F Z O O T
D N U O R G R E D N U N O D N O L C R A
E V O L I D D A W P O C I E T S H O J T
D M N B E R Y L O B Y T P P E L L M N I
T D I S J O J T Y C B A P M S N P B E O
X U N Y T O W O O T C R F T O J I R O N
```

Pongleton
Frampton Hotel
Dog Lead
Pearl Necklace
Beryl
Slocomb
Footprint

London Underground
Tuppy
Inspector Caird
Waddilove
Lighthearted
Grudges
Spinster

Tube Station
Mavis Doriel Hay
Basil
Red Herrings
Lies
Disinheritance

KRISS KROSS
The Z Murders by J. Jefferson Farjeon

Place into the grid the words listed below and then, using the letters highlighted therein, spell out a short story collection in the British Library Crime Classics series.

4 Letters
Taxi

5 Letters
Amble
Chase
Diggs
Drugs
Hotel
Plane
Token
Train

6 Letters
Dutton
Euston
Sylvia

7 Letters
Farjeon
Handbag
Snoring
Villain

8 Letters
Armchair

Fogbound
Fugitive
Thriller
Winifred

9 Letters
Melodrama
Temperley

12 Letters
Metal Mammoth
Serial Killer

CROSSWORD

All of the clues are for words found in the titles and authors contained in the British Library short story collection *Crimson Snow*. The highlighted letters spell out the surname of an author from the series.

Down

1. The word which completes this Miss Marple short story: 'A — Tragedy'. (9)

4. A first name which links a volcano, a song by The Carpenters and a spacecraft. (3)

5. One of the five senses. (5)

7. The first name of Napoleon Bonaparte's first wife. (9)

10. A rhododendron is a type of this. (4)

12. The surname of the surgeon who inspired Arthur Conan Doyle's creation of Sherlock Holmes. (4)

14. The word which completes this title by Dashiell Hammett: *The Thin —*. (3)

16. A preposition which can be followed by hand and side. (3)

Across

2. The surname of Hercule Poirot's Watson-like sidekick. (8)

3. The last month of the year to have 31 days. (8)

6. A word to describe a profound thought. (4)

8. An informal word for dismissal from work. (4)

9. The surname of a Scottish knight involved in fighting the English in the Wars of Scottish Independence. (7)

11. One of the four suits in a pack of cards. (4)

13. These can be found on your roof and in your bathroom. (5)

15. A group of vocal performers who are often found outside people's homes. (5, 7)

PATH FINDER PUZZLE
The Lake District Murder by John Bude

Using the highlighted starting letter trace a path through
the letters following the order of the words listed below.

I	C	T	J	A	I	G	R	A	T	I	O
R	O	T	K	C	M	R	E	K	N	M	N
T	N	Y	C	E	E	D	R	I	A	O	N
S	L	A	L	V	D	U	A	V	T	Y	E
I	I	A	D	I	T	F	R	E	I	T	E
D	L	E	E	M	O	E	L	R	H	A	H
E	Y	R	I	U	C	Y	C	S	W	V	E
K	A	I	C	S	R	O	P	M	L	I	N
E	L	D	E	E	O	T	A	O	C	O	M
G	V	R	M	G	M	Y	N	I	C	E	A
A	I	E	U	A	G	P	O	L	R	O	R
L	L	D	R	R	A	R	A	C	T	P	Y

1. Garage
2. Suicide
3. Murder
4. Village
5. Lake District
6. Jack Clayton
7. Lily Reade
8. Motive
9. Emigration
10. Money
11. Tanker Drivers
12. White Haven
13. Maryport
14. Car
15. Police
16. Oil Company
17. Motorcycle
18. Fraud

WORD SEARCH

All the words listed below relate to John Bude's
The Cornish Coast Murder (1935). The words are
hidden in the grid horizontally, vertically, diagonally and
backwards.

```
U F O I O D D P U L Y S G N I L Y E R G D
U D Z E C C H U H C U O R G C P S I X X O
I H A I O H E T A R T S I G A M V F R U C
E X E A T K C O H S L L E H S H O U D X T
L T A U B C O N V A A M N A V K Y L H E O
L F R R P O E E O E U U U G C A A E D U R
E L E U M W T R E G A R T H A N O J Q V P
W D F N A C V I C A R A G E O E J W R M E
S E U C Y A H F T Y E U O R A Y A N E Y N
G V S B A E M A T K N V P X U U R T P Z D
I O S R N O F U I U T N E V U P U A W D R
B L D V C H D I E R E I S R U I Y Y O X I
R N M X E N O Z W H D S T R E C K R C Q L
O E E H P H T J O D T E N A L M E P P S L
T D F E I S E W C M I A T Y A T W E I O T
C D B G A L A O C X H M P E F T A D A E U
E I M O D M R E H C A O P F C E Y Y O Z N
P B C Y O N E O A J U E T R F T J E D R D
S R J F W S D R U S S U W O C I I E M S Q
N O S A E O H E T G B A C V A I L V Y R I
I F L E O R E V E R E N D D O D D C E E E
O L E R C U U E Y A F H F N E E N Z Q S A
```

Reverend Dodd	Doctor Pendrill	Forbidden Love
Greylings	Magistrate	Inspector Bigswell
PC Grouch	Tregarthan	John Bude
Shell Shock	Armchair Detectives	Boscawen
Ronald	Ruth	Cowper
Cornwall	Poacher	Coast
Midwife	Vicarage	

KRISS KROSS
Death in the Tunnel by Miles Burton

Place into the grid the words listed below and then, using the letters highlighted therein, spell out another title from the British Library Crime Classics series.

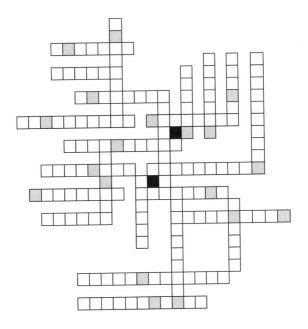

6 Letters
Arnold
Burton
Puzzle
Ticket
Tunnel
Winter

7 Letters
Desmond
Saxonby
Suicide

8 Letters
Red Light
Howdunit
Initials
Shooting
November

9 Letters
Bank Notes
Stourford

10 Letters
Conspiracy
First Class
Locked Room
Locomotive
Magistrate
Passengers

11 Letters
Businessman

13 Letters
Criminologist

CROSS OUT

Cross out any letters in the grid below that appear
more than once and rearrange the remaining letters
to reveal the title of one of Dorothy L. Sayers' short
stories.

C	W	U	E	H	R	Q	Z	L
I	Y	P	D	N	K	C	G	E
G	M	R	J	Z	I	M	H	D
V	K	C	Q	T	U	J	W	Q
D	W	N	G	E	F	P	V	S
P	H	F	J	I	D	R	C	H
R	Z	O	W	M	B	U	N	I
A	Q	U	G	C	V	K	D	E

ADD A LETTER

Make a new word by adding one letter to the words on the left-hand side, with the help of the accompanying clue on the right. The letter added goes into the middle column. At the end, this column should spell out the first name of an author from the British Library Crime Classics series.

FAME		Something you do to a picture
BARN		A Scottish word for a child
FORE		Often preceded by the word 'air'
TREAD		Something to sew a button on with
HERD		Listened to something
WANING		E.g. a red light
MEAL		Recognition of bravery

ADD THE VOWELS

Add in the vowels missing from each of these titles from the British Library Crime Classics series. Vowels could go before, in the middle or after the letters given below.

1. TH NCRDBL CRM

2. DTH F NTN

3. NTDT T VNM

4. DTH F N RMN

5. DTH N TH RVR

6. MRDR N TH MSM

7. MR BZLGTTS GNT

8. TH PSND CHCLTS CS

9. TH DD SHLL B RSD

10. TH CRNSH CST MRDR

WORD SEARCH

All the words listed below relate to John Rowland's *Calamity in Kent* (1950). The words are hidden in the grid horizontally, vertically, diagonally and backwards.

```
E Z E Y L D N A L W O R U Y S C F A Q U U
Y E I N O W G B W H E F J N K H Y J M Z U
T Q N N C C I N F D R A D I I A E V P X G
A E A O V M B S I I W I A Z L R J C R Z A
P F K H D R F N W N N T X C B R O R I Z Y
J E V R E N S N I I O W L L E I U I N M F
F E M L A E O M O I D I Z U C N R N S D L
M I S I A M H L P T F U T S K G N S P Y B
E W G S R Y K F Y F E T A A I T A P E F R
P P I C Q C T C R M G B P O R O L E C D O
N D J Y O X E A A N M T O W I N I C T T A
E C O I D N I L I L A I E O N H S T O T D
A T I O M L V B B M B A J Z K O T O R E G
T Y L B W T B A H I A U I O B T I R B Z A
U N X A O A I U L N S L T E P E I S E E T
T O Y Q T J J L O E N S U T Q L Z H E N E
S N E S V C G M S U S E O U P T K E C I W
H M E D L T M O Y L T C X P E F C L H I Y
P B I K I W E O O O E R E I M M S L E Q E
P H O O R N Z E P B K Y J N A I U E N I U
P O O C S R E P A P S W E N C E Y Y Y Z R
N O M E R I A S U I S Y O L A E I V M E X
```

Seaside	Broadgate	Cliff Railway
Stabbing	Jimmy London	Kent
Journalist	Rowland	Aloysius
Inspector Beech	Skilbeck	Notebook
Convalescence	Inspector Shelley	Black Market
Newspaper Scoop	Impossible Crime	Jim Tilsley
Rationing	Charrington Hotel	

CROSSWORD

All of the clues are for words found in the titles contained in the British Library short story collection *Murder at the Manor*. The highlighted letters spell out the surname of an author from the series.

Down

1. A difficulty which needs to be dealt with. (7)

3. A metal with the chemical symbol Cu. (6)

5. Tennyson's 'Mariana' resided in such a moated location. (6)

6. Notes or diagrams written down to aid the completion of the task. (4)

7. The word which completes this film title: — *Prefer Blondes*. (9)

9. In the Bible Samson destroys a Philistine temple by pushing against these. (7)

12. Surname of the novelist who wrote *East Lynne*. (4)

14. The word which completes this title by Anthony Berkeley: *The Second* —. (4)

Across

2. Bay and casement are two types of this. (6)

4. Something which can be sent in a code or by pigeon. (7)

8. A room in the home usually found near the front door. (4)

9. Participants in a game. (7)

10. One of the places where drawings of dancing men are left in the Holmes short story, 'The Adventure of the Dancing Men'. (7)

11. There are famous examples of this type of building in London, Paris and Pisa. (5)

13. Deciduous trees often found in Europe and North America. (7)

15. An extreme sense of shock or fear. (6)

16. What the biblical prophet Jeremiah was thrown into. (4)

ADD A LETTER

Make a new word by adding one letter to the words on the left-hand side, with the help of the accompanying clue on the right. The letter added goes into the middle column. At the end, this column should spell out a location mentioned in the title of a British Library Crime Classics novel.

POSER		Something displayed on a wall
SELF		An upholder of literature
WEAK		To cause or inflict
BEST		Beauty and the _____
RUMBLE		A fruity dessert
SEWER		An item used on grills or with fondue
BANK		Empty
SPAR		Weapon with a pointed tip
CANON		Another name for a gorge

WORD SEARCH

There are 18 characters from Christie's novels to be found in the grid below. They can be found horizontally, vertically, diagonally and backwards.

E	W	O	E	J	T	E	N	Y	P	I	Y	P	S	U	Y	I
U	N	I	Q	D	Q	O	S	X	L	S	A	Y	A	J	H	N
B	E	R	E	S	F	O	R	D	T	T	E	H	C	T	A	R
U	C	U	T	O	R	I	O	P	L	H	D	N	M	L	D	E
Y	K	E	G	E	O	O	B	T	U	E	O	W	E	W	G	F
A	U	Q	E	E	A	E	N	C	E	O	Y	R	D	A	A	D
E	R	M	A	M	L	M	A	Y	P	W	L	E	L	R	C	E
Y	H	I	H	N	D	P	E	Z	R	M	E	H	I	G	K	R
A	E	H	A	X	N	R	R	U	J	U	U	I	T	R	R	E
C	U	T	G	D	I	I	B	A	O	O	F	J	O	A	O	I
I	E	A	N	X	N	Y	U	R	M	E	C	E	L	V	Y	M
I	B	O	O	T	K	E	R	Q	S	E	L	E	C	E	D	P
D	I	P	M	E	U	C	O	Q	Y	D	N	T	O	N	Y	C
G	W	X	E	S	G	S	G	L	N	E	Y	A	T	I	F	G
T	M	N	L	R	O	Y	E	U	I	J	L	D	J	A	F	I
O	E	R	V	C	I	D	B	A	A	V	A	R	Y	W	B	O
S	P	J	Y	Z	O	I	P	U	F	A	E	P	A	C	E	I
L	U	V	H	A	S	T	I	N	G	S	J	R	P	H	E	M

Pyne	Ruby Keene	Ariadne Oliver	Japp
Lemon	Redfern	Harley Quin	Hastings
Ratchett	Battle	Doyle	Wargrave
Clotilde	Ackroyd	Bundle	Poirot
Jane Marple	Beresford		

CROSSWORD

All of the clues are for words found in the titles contained in the British Library short story collection *Miraculous Mysteries*. The highlighted letters spell out the surname of an author from the series.

Down

1. An occupation which became open to men in the UK in 1829. (9)

2. An evergreen herb used in cooking. (5)

5. The type of weapon used in Ngaio Marsh's debut, *A Man Lay Dead*. (6)

6. In three parables told by Jesus, the coin, the sheep and the son all have this in common. (4)

9. Such as a halberd, a crossbow or a revolver. (6)

11. The civilisation which invented the watermill, democracy and the screw. (5)

12. Such as Jesus' act of turning water into wine. (7)

15. The type of home many of the suspects in John Bude's *Death on the Riviera* reside in. (5)

Across

3. Such as a kitchen or a lounge. (4)

4. A word which can be followed by life, rhyme and board. (4)

7. The word which completes this title by Josephine Tey: *The Singing* —. (5)

8. A street of terraced housing which forms an arc; a setting which can be found in Christie's *The Clocks*. (8)

10. A television or radio transmission. (9)

13. Gravity, radio waves and air can all be described using this word. (9)

14. An adjective to describe something or someone who is different in an exceptional or noteworthy way. (7)

16. A soft non-magnetic metal from the boron group. (9)

17. A synonym for being intelligent. (6)

WORD SEARCH

There are eighteen characters from Sayers' novels to be found in the grid below. They can be found horizontally, vertically, diagonally and backwards.

```
D E O P O O R U S J G Y I N O D E R B
T N R Y O P C R L B P K I T D V F A I
O C E I F E A R D U F Y E V N E A X G
O A J E C U E P H I L I P B O Y E S A
P F E I I K D O N D A I B E Y C T T N
N N D E R A J M L U Q C A E D E G E A
A R K A O D A J A K I O R L L I E I E
M I P J S D A G D E L U B O V D N R D
B B R G D B P C Y O E S U H A R E R R
U J C O Q J F L M F T M T I G A R A O
N G F F N U Y I A D I S H O G G A H T
T G H V X O P M R E T M N G E A L H C
E V X N Y N H P Y N I O O U E L F H I
R N F F F O W S I V A E T I U E E S V
M D C C A A R O A E M J R I G D N E S
U U I U N M U N J R A H N F A I T L F
T L Y I G H Z Q B U R X T G T M I B A
I I O T O D O G N M T E T Y N M M R X
P K Y R I M P E Y B I G G S O E A U U
P E T E R W U Q P K N I N E M F N M I
```

General Fentiman	Montague Egg	Duke of Denver
Bredon	Impey Biggs	Letitia Martin
Climpson	Parker	Victor Dean
Murbles	Honoria	Peter
Delagardie	Arbuthnot	Philip Boyes
Lady Mary	Bunter	Harriet

WORD SEARCH

All the words listed below relate to Agatha Christie's *Murder on the Orient Express* (1934). The words are hidden in the grid horizontally, vertically, diagonally and backwards.

```
K T A X J E N I T N A T S N O C U E K
A P A D A J T N E E U Q C A M T N C E
U G X E H T E E O W U T D M I C H E L
E R F F N C L C E E O U D E V A O O Y
J H W I A W A T E R G D A I T E N P B
E Q E K W I V O O L T M N B M U M O I
R S U I U T Y I C Q O C O I P H T C L
R P A D C T Z A Q S O X H Y W U C A I
I O I N U E Y T I A I M R I F N N S U
U E A A Y S M H U I P A S F F K E P O
U X Q P D S F Y E R N T L J W I Z P I
H I T P A A B C V O A U X A M M N O O
L U Y E I C D N I N A R S R C O H E O
T E B R S A X S B B O E E I S N P S T
A O S B Y B S U R Y A H H F Y O P O O
A R O I A I L I N O E Y F T R A I N R
J O X U M R G J U S T I C E O E U P I
C V L Y X T D P I P E C L E A N E R O
Y N R E T T E L D E N R U B S N O W P
F E I H C R E K D N A H I O U U C Y N
```

Train	Hat Box	Snow	Poirot
Cassetti	Daisy	Kidnapper	Burned Letter
Kimono	Pipe Cleaner	MacQueen	Hubbard
Schmidt	Istanbul	Justice	Calais Coach
Handkerchief	Constantine	Michel	Open Window
Valet	Missionary		

CROSSWORD

All of the clues are for words found in the titles
contained in the British Library short story collection
Silent Nights. The highlighted letters spell out the
surname of an author from the series.

Down

2. The room into which the spider invites the fly in Mary Howitt's poem of 1829. (7)

3. These can be found at Madame Tussauds. (8)

5. A word to describe a red jewel or an unpleasant abscess or boil. (9)

6. What is revealed when all the suspects are gathered at the end of the case. (8)

7. Something given to a child when they are born. (4)

11. The nationality of Robert Van Gulik's fictional sleuth, Judge Dee. (7)

12. In Christopher St John Sprigg's *Death of an Airman* and Christie's *Death in the Clouds*, murder takes place during this activity. (6)

13. There are five of these on the Chinese flag. (5)

Across

1. A synonym of cheerful. (5)

4. An item so valuable that in the parable the man gave everything he had so he could obtain it. (5)

6. Used to pad out furniture or toys. (8)

8. The person appointed to manage the finances of a group or organisation. (9)

9. A fruit whose seeds contain amygdalin, which releases cyanide when it interacts with digestive enzymes. (5)

10. The act of leaving in a hurry, usually to avoid arrest. (10)

14. The item which is stolen in Agatha Christie's short story: 'The Jewel Robbery at the Grand Metropolitan'. (8)

15. Such as The Cabinet Escape and The French Drop. (6)

KRISS KROSS
The Santa Klaus Murder
by Mavis Doriel Hay

Place into the grid the words listed below and then, using the letters highlighted therein, spell out the surname of an author from the British Library Crime Classics series.

3 Letters
Hay
Map
Kit

4 Letters
Earl
Feud
Will

5 Letters
Actor
Study
Alibi
Spite

6 Letters
Bullet
Dittie
Police

7 Letters
Mildred
Melbury
Wynford
Library

8 Letters
Flaxmere
Costumes

9 Letters
Christmas
Chauffeur
Crewkerne

10 Letters
Santa Klaus
Haulmshire

12 Letters
Country House

OUT NOW IN PAPERBACK

"The British Library's classic crime project …
sees long-lost novels rediscovered and
published for a new generation."
Telegraph

"Classic crime novels [are] brought back
to life by the British Library."
The Times

"[The British Library's] growing list of 1930s/1940s/
1950s classics crime novels, with some of the best
covers I have seen for many a day, is so well chosen."
Susan Hill, Jacob's Room is Full of Books

"Of course, you can't go wrong with any
of the British Library Crime Classics."
The Washington Post

ANSWERS

p5 Odd One Out
1. *Mystery in the Channel*, as all the others have victims killed in aeroplanes.
2. *Somebody at the Door*, as all the others were published in the 1930s.
3. *Death Makes a Prophet*, as all the others have college settings.
4. *The Hog's Back Mystery*, as all the others have female killers.
5. *A Scream in Soho*, as all the others take place during the Christmas season.

p6 Kriss Kross
Author's Surname: Postgate

p8 Crossword
Down: 1. Alibi 2. Interrogation
3. Clue 4. Confess 8. Red Herrings
9. Floorplan 10. Fugitive 11. Poison
Across: 5. Bloodstain 6. Criminal
7. Suspects 10. Frame-up 12. Pistol
13. Footprint 14. Dagger
British Library Authors:
(Miles) Burton and (Gil) North

p10 Cross Out
Curtain, a word which also features in Alan Melville's *Quick Curtain*

p11 Who Was Killed?
Emily Inglethorp – *The Mysterious Affair at Styles*
Gerald Wade – *The Seven Dials Mystery*
Alex Pritchard – *Why Didn't They Ask Evans?*
Paul Renauld – *The Murder on the Links*

Samuel Ratchett – *Murder on the Orient Express*
Arlena Marshall – *Evil Under the Sun*

p12 Word Wheel
Gil North

p13 Word Search

p14 Path Finder Puzzle

p15 Spot the Titles
Agatha Christie Titles: *Third Girl*, *Endless Night*, *Sleeping Murder*, *At Bertram's Hotel* and *After the Funeral*
Dorothy L. Sayers Titles: *Unnatural Death* and *Gaudy Night*
British Library Titles: *Quick Curtain*, *Seven Dead*, *Antidote to Venom*,

144

Thirteen Guests, Silent Nights, Murder Underground, Miraculous Mysteries and *Calamity in Kent*

p16 Crossword

Down: 1. Foreign 3. Quack
5. Prophets 6. Family 9. Serpents
11. Calamity 14. Tunnel
16. Stands 17. Arm

Across: 2. Door 4. Case 7. Curtain
8. Back 9. Snow 10. Lake 12. Square
13. Capital 15. Guests 17. Airman
British Library Author: (Charles)
Warren Adams

p18 Kriss Kross

British Library Crime Classics Title:
Murder of a Lady

p20 Who Was Killed?

Agatha Dawson – *Unnatural Death*
Philip Boyes – *Strong Poison*
Paul Alexis – *Have His Carcase*
George Harrison – *The Documents in the Case*
Sandy Campbell – *The Five Red Herrings*
Victor Dean – *Murder Must Advertise*

p21 Who Am I?

Anthony Wynne – A
George Bellairs – B
John Bude – C
Gil North – D
Freeman Wills Crofts – E

p22 Word Search

p23 Spot the Titles

Agatha Christie Titles: *Murder is Easy, Crooked House, Ordeal by Innocence, Sparkling Cyanide* and *The Sittaford Mystery*
Dorothy L. Sayers Titles: *Strong Poison* and *Murder Must Advertise*
British Library Titles: *Continental Crimes, Death on the Cherwell, The Z Murders, Resorting to Murder, The Incredible Crime, Death in the Tunnel, Murder of a Lady* and *The Female Detective*

p24 Word Wheel

Seven Dead

p25 Add a Letter

Bellairs

p26 Odd One Out

1. *4:50 from Paddington*, as all the others have bodies found inside trains whilst in this Christie novel the first victim is killed in a train but the body is found elsewhere.
2. *The Cheltenham Square Murder*, as all the others use being shot as the primary victim's murder method.
3. *The Methods of Sergeant Cluff*,

as all the others primary murder victims are male.

4. *The Notting Hill Mystery*, as all the others use animals significantly either in the creation or setting up of their central crimes.

5. *Thirteen Guests*, as all the others were published in the 1940s.

p27 Cross Out

The Big Four

p28 Word Search

p29 Spot the Titles

Agatha Christie Titles: *Lord Edgware Dies, Sad Cypress, Dumb Witness, The Clocks* and *Five Little Pigs*
Dorothy L. Sayers Titles: *Busman's Honeymoon* and *Five Red Herrings*
British Library Titles: *Death of Anton, Mystery in White, Crimson Snow, Mr Bazalgette's Agent, Foreign Bodies, Murder in Piccadilly, Family Matters* and *The Poisoned Chocolates Case*

p30 Crossword

Down: 1. Manor 2. From
3. Revelation 5. Secret 6. Sussex
9. Poisoned 10. White 12. Portrait
14. Murderer 17. Venom

Across: 4. Somebody 6. Scream
7. Silent 8. Verdict 11. Notting Hill
13. Museum 15. Sergeant 16. Seven
18. Mr 19. Underground
British Library Author: (John G.) Brandon

p32 Add a Letter

Rowland

p33 Odd One Out

1. *Murder of a Lady*, as all the others use stabbing as their primary victim's murder method.

2. *Family Matters*, as all the others have a character who it is assumed has disappeared, but in fact has been murdered.

3. *Murder in Piccadilly*, as all the others involve drug smuggling.

4. *The Cornish Coast Murder*, as all the others involve poisonings.

5. *Death in the Riviera*, as all the others were published in 1936.

p34 Who Am I?

Miles Burton – A
Andrew Forrester – B
J. Jefferson Farjeon – C
Christopher St John Sprigg – D
Raymond Postgate – E

p35 Add the Vowels

1. Murder is Easy
2. Evil Under the Sun
3. Taken at the Flood
4. After the Funeral
5. Murder in Mesopotamia
6. And Then There Were None
7. Cat Among the Pigeons
8. The Pale Horse
9. At Bertram's Hotel
10. Elephants Can Remember

A	E	L	E	E	A	L	I	O	S	P	E
T	D	V	M	S	S	E	I	N	N	T	C
H	E	I	N	Y	T	D	R	P	I	O	R
O	L	L	A	D	T	E	I	V	E	I	M
F	N	T	L	E	E	C	T	D	R	N	T
A	O	I	A	M	O	G	N	E	U	M	O
N	T	G	E	R	C	S	I	R	W	Y	C
N	T	R	A	C	C	U	D	D	E	E	O
W	Z	E	P	I	R	P	H	C	A	R	N
O	E	T	I	S	J	E	T	R	E	G	F
L	A	R	S	T	O	S	A	N	T	I	E
C	O	D	O	D	R	E	M	O	I	S	S

Alex Restarick – *They Do It With Mirrors*

p54 Cross Out
John Bude

p55 Add a letter
Gil North

p56 Location, Location, Location
Devon – *Evil Under the Sun*
Dartmoor – *The Sittaford Mystery*
Cape Town – *The Man in the Brown Suit*
Lymstock – *The Moving Finger*
Morocco – *Destination Unknown*
Chipping Cleghorn – *A Murder is Announced*

p57 Word Wheel
Inspector

p58 Path Finder Puzzle

p59 Odd One Out
1. *Mystery in the Channel*, as all the others have deaths which are first considered suicides but are actually murders.

2. *Seven Dead*, as all the others have deaths which are first considered accidents but are actually murders.

3. *Whose Body?*, as all the others are country house murder mysteries.

4. *The Notting Hill Mystery*, as all the others are short story collections.

5. *Death of Anton*, as all the others include amateur detectives.

p60 Crossword
Down: 1. Marble 2. Cannon 4. Flat
5. Cheese 6. Street 8. Hands
9. Puzzle 11. Casket 12. Mask 15. Leaf
Across: 3. Wind 6. Silver 7. Hang
10. House 11. Chance 13. East
14. Tragedy 16. Little
British Library Author: (Lois)
Austen-Leigh

p62 Add a Letter
Piccadilly

p63 Word Search

p64 Who Am I?
Mavis Doriel Hay – A
Alan Melville – B
John Rowland – C
John G. Brandon – D
Anthony Rolls – E

Distorted Covers

p65

p66

p67

p68

p69

p70

p71

p72

p73

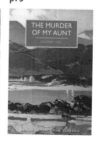

Spot the Difference

p74

p76

p78

p80

p82

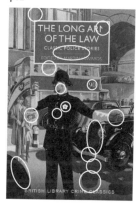

p84

p86

p88

p90 Snapshot Covers I

p91 Snapshot Covers 2

p92 Snapshot Covers 3

p93 Snapshot Covers 4

p94 Snapshot Covers 5

p95 Snapshot Covers 6

p96 Kriss Kross

British Library Crime Classics title:
The Lake District Murder

p98 Odd One Out

1. *Somebody at the Door*, as all the others are inverted mysteries.

2. *Weekend at Thrackley*, as all the others are partially or wholly structured around a murder trial.

3. *Murder in Piccadilly*, as all the others are set during WW2.

4. *Bats in the Belfry*, as all the others are set in Devon.

5. *Portrait of a Murderer*, as all the other novels have a character named Meredith, whilst this one was written by someone called Meredith.

p99 Path Finder Puzzle

S	C	E	S	E	A	S	S	U	I	T	C
E	H	L	E	V	G	D	O	R	E	S	A
E	A	R	T	U	S	R	B	I	N	S	P
Y	O	L	T	M	T	A	B	Y	R	O	E
I	R	P	M	E	S	N	E	R	H	T	C
H	D	C	L	M	O	A	L	L	O	M	E
T	I	A	A	S	S	R	Y	W	T	I	R
S	N	R	T	G	G	E	G	A	R	F	F
E	W	E	N	N	E	O	R	L	U	U	E
G	A	H	R	I	L	Y	E	T	D	G	E
L	O	R	Y	G	R	A	R	J	A	Y	R
L	I	C	N	U	O	C	Y	A	N	U	A

p100 Crossword

Down: 1. Edge 2. Simpson 3. Links 5. Task 6. Holiday 7. Removed 9. Adventure 10. Finger 12. Abroad 15. Stone 17. Razor
Across: 4. Ice 8. Schoolmaster 11. Cousin 13. Bentley 14. Golf 16. Posteriori 18. Hazel 19. Foot
British Library Author: Anthony Rolls

p102 Word Search

p103 Add a Letter

Brynmawr

p104 Location, Location, Location

Birmingham Zoo – *Antidote to Venom*
Shufflecester – *Family Matters*
King Poplars – *Portrait of a Murderer*
Oxford – *Death on the Cherwell*
Hilary Magna – *Death of a Busybody*
Cambridge – *The Incredible Crime*

p105 Word Wheel

Poisoned

p106 Path Finder Puzzle

O	W	H	D	R	P	E	R	O	M	T	S
R	L	O	E	A	R	A	R	C	L	E	E
R	I	R	E	T	M	K	C	H	E	R	N
A	D	T	M	T	A	I	A	E	R	Y	A
S	A	Y	I	R	E	L	L	R	U	M	L
R	U	O	S	S	B	N	B	D	E	R	D
E	D	B	H	G	O	O	A	M	R	E	O
R	I	T	H	I	E	N	P	U	M	M	U
E	M	T	R	E	G	E	N	S	E	B	S
N	T	N	E	E	T	Y	C	A	R	A	R
I	E	N	D	E	I	S	Q	U	R	C	N
R	E	P	U	S	R	W	E	M	I	T	E

p107 Word Wheel

Sergeant

p108 Kriss Kross

British Library Crime Classics Title:
The Hog's Back Mystery

p110 Word Wheel

Kingston

p111 Word Search

p112 Kriss Kross

Authors' Surnames: Forrester and
Crofts

p114 Crossword

Down: 1. Impossible 2. Winter
3. Hog 4. Murder 6. Shall 9. Quick
12. Agent 14. Twelve
16. Makes 18. Firm
Across: 5. Busybody 7. Santa
8. Croydon 10. Law 11. Miraculous
13. Kent 15. Chocolates 17. Coast
19. Thirteen 20. Female
British Library Author: Mavis
Doriel Hay

p116 Add a Letter

Macdonald

p117 Word Search

p118 Kriss Kross

British Library Short Story
Collection: *Crimson Snow*

p120 Crossword

Down: 1. Christmas 4. Eve
5. Touch 7. Josephine 10. Bush
12. Bell 14. Man 16. Off
Across: 2. Hastings 3. December
6. Deep 8. Sack 9. Wallace
11. Club 13. Tiles 15. Carol Singers
British Library Author:
(Christopher St John) Sprigg

p122 Path Finder Puzzle

I	C	T	J	A	I	G	R	A	T	I	O
R	O	T	K	C	M	R	E	K	N	M	N
T	N	Y	C	E	E	D	R	I	A	O	N
S	L	A	L	V	D	U	A	V	T	Y	E
I	I	A	D	I	T	F	R	E	I	T	E
D	L	E	E	M	O	E	L	R	H	A	H
E	Y	R	I	U	C	Y	C	S	W	V	E
K	A	I	C	S	R	O	P	M	L	I	N
E	L	D	E	E	O	T	A	O	C	O	M
G	V	R	M	G	M	Y	N	I	C	E	A
A	I	E	U	A	G	P	O	L	R	O	R
L	L	D	R	R	A	R	A	C	T	P	Y

p123 Word Search

p124 Kriss Kross

British Library Crime Classics Title:
Mystery in the Channel

p126 Cross Out

Talboys

p127 Add a Letter

Richard

p128 Add the Vowels

1. The Incredible Crime
2. Death of Anton
3. Antidote To Venom
4. Death of an Airman
5. Death on the Riviera
6. Murder in the Museum
7. Mr Bazalgette's Agent
8. The Poisoned Chocolates Case
9. The Dead Shall Be Raised
10. The Cornish Coast Murder

p129 Word Search

p130 Crossword

Down: 1. Problem 3. Copper
5. Grange 6. Plan 7. Gentlemen
9. Pillars 12. Wood 14. Shot
Across: 2. Window 4. Message
8. Hall 9. Players 10. Sundial
11. Tower 13. Beeches 15. Horror
16. Well
British Library Author: (John)
Rowland

p132 Add a Letter

Thrackley

p133 Word Search

p134 Crossword

Down: 1. Policeman 2. Thyme
5. Dagger 6. Lost 9. Weapon
11. Greek 12. Miracle 15. Villa
Across: 3. Room 4. Half 7. Sands
8. Crescent 10. Broadcast
13. Invisible 14. Special
16. Aluminium 17. Clever
British Library Author: (Charles)
Kingston

p136 Word Search

p137 Word Search

p138 Crossword

Down: 2. Parlour 3. Waxworks
5. Carbuncle 6. Solution 7. Name
11. Chinese 12. Flying 13. Stars
Across: 1. Happy 4. Pearl 6. Stuffing
8. Treasurer 9. Apple 10. Absconding
14. Necklace 15. Tricks
British Library Author: (Freeman
Wills) Crofts

p140 Kriss Kross

Author's Surname: Berkeley

BRITISH LIBRARY CRIME CLASSICS SERIES

Death of a Busybody – George Bellairs
The Poisoned Chocolates Case – Anthony Berkeley
Crimson Snow – ed. Martin Edwards
The Dead Shall be Raised & Murder of a Quack – George Bellairs
Verdict of Twelve – Raymond Postgate
Scarweather – Anthony Rolls
Family Matters – Anthony Rolls
Miraculous Mysteries – ed. Martin Edwards
The Incredible Crime – Lois Austen-Leigh
Continental Crimes – ed. Martin Edwards
Death Makes a Prophet – John Bude
The Long Arm of the Law – ed. Martin Edwards
Portrait of a Murderer – Anne Meredith
Seven Dead – J. Jefferson Farjeon
Foreign Bodies – ed. Martin Edwards
Somebody at the Door – Raymond Postgate
Bats in the Belfry – E.C.R. Lorac
Fire in the Thatch – E.C.R. Lorac
Blood on the Tracks – ed. Martin Edwards
The Murder of My Aunt – Richard Hull
Excellent Intentions – Richard Hull
Weekend at Thrackley – Alan Melville
The Arsenal Stadium Mystery – Leonard Gribble
The Division Bell Mystery – Ellen Wilkinson
The Belting Inheritance – Julian Symons
The Colour of Murder – Julian Symons
The Christmas Card Crime – ed. Martin Edwards
Murder by Matchlight – E.C.R. Lorac

Also Available
The Story of Classic Crime in 100 Books – Martin Edwards

**Many of our titles are also available in
eBook and audio editions**